101 ANIMAL STORIES

DREAMLAND PUBLICATIONS

J-128, Kirti Nagar, New Delhi-110 015, India
Tel : +91-11-2510 6050, 2543 5657
E-mail : dreamland@dreamlandpublications.com
Shop online at www.dreamlandpublications.com
Follow us on www.instagram.com/dreamland.publications

Published in 2022 by
DREAMLAND PUBLICATIONS
J-128, Kirti Nagar, New Delhi - 110 015, India
Tel : +91-11-2510 6050, 2543 5657
E-mail : dreamland@dreamlandpublications.com, www.dreamlandpublications.com
Printed in India

Contents

1. THE TOWN MOUSE AND THE COUNTRY MOUSE

Once, the town mouse invited the country mouse to his house. When the country mouse went to the town mouse's house, he asked him, "Why do you all live inside such houses? Don't you go out and play much?" The town mouse said, "No, we don't go out much as there are many vehicles on the road, and too many people walking around." Later, the town mouse went to the country mouse's house in the countryside. He said to the country mouse, "You are so lucky that you live here. At least you get fresh air to breath." The country mouse told the town mouse that it is better to be satisfied with what we have and where we live. Only then will we be able to live happily.

Moral: Be content with what you have.

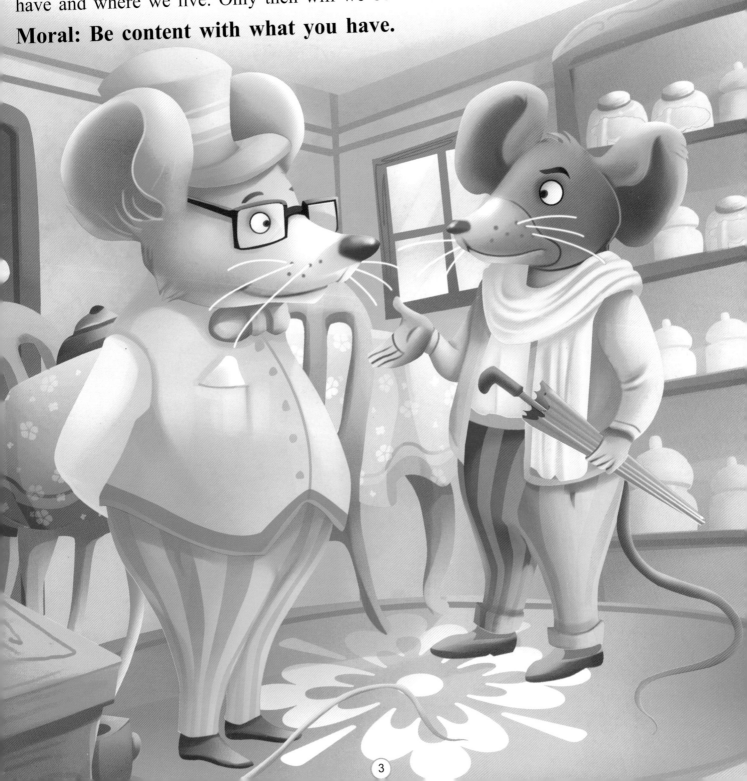

2. THE BLUE-DYED JACKAL

A jackal fell into a blue-dye barrel one day. "Oh no, I'm completely blue," he cried. As he walked into the jungle returning to his home, the animals thought he was a strange new animal. "Let me fool these animals by telling them I am from heaven," he thought to himself cleverly. And for sure he did the same. All the animals, including the lion, the elephant, the donkey, the foxes, and the monkeys were present. Suddenly at a distance, a group of jackals started to shout at the top of their voice. Hearing their voices, the blue-dyed jackal couldn't help but shout back in response. At once the animals knew who this strange animal was and started to beat him up, turning him naturally blue.

Moral: Do not lie about who you indeed are.

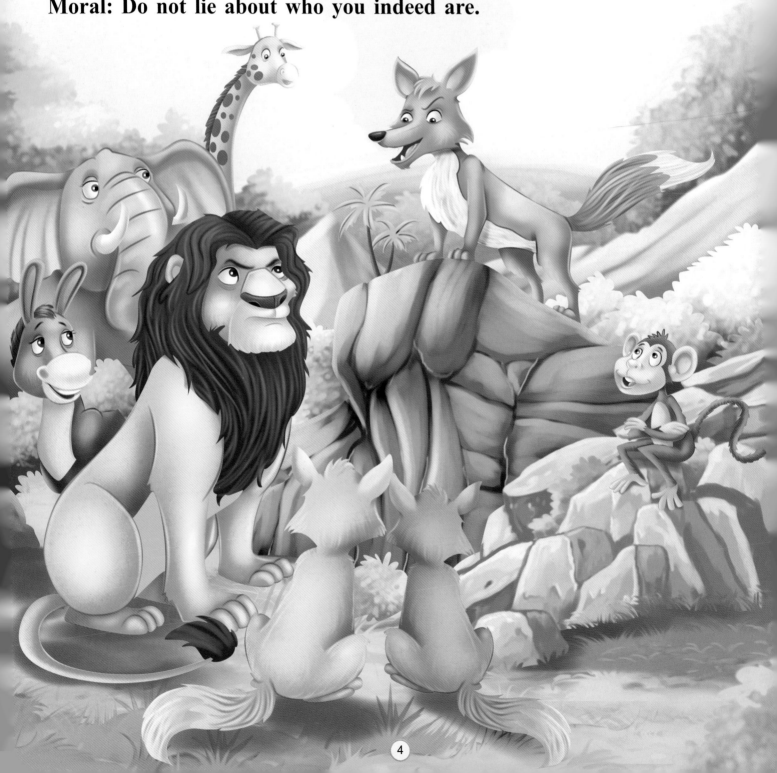

3. THE WOLF AND THE HERON

A wolf got a fishbone stuck in his throat and ran to a heron for help. "Please help me! I will reward you handsomely for your kindness." The heron reached down his throat with his long beak. Slowly and carefully, he pulled out the fishbone from the wolf's throat. Relieved, the wolf sat for a minute, breathing heavily, feeling grateful to be alive, got up, and started to walk away. "Hey! You promised me a handsome reward. Why are you leaving?" the heron asked as he tried to stop the wolf. "You see my friend. I did not bite your head off when you put your beak inside my mouth. That was my handsome and generous gift," the wolf said and hopped away.

Moral: Do not trust strangers so easily.

4. THE JEALOUS SOLE

A group of fish decided to select a king for themselves. "We should select a king to maintain peace and order among us." A wise fish added, "A race should be held, and the fastest fish would be selected as the king." Everyone thought about it for some time. After finding no other way, the fishes agreed and took part in the race. They found that the herring had come first. But the sole felt very jealous and twisted its mouth. Since then, the sole's mouth has remained twisted on one side. This was considered as its punishment!

Moral: We should never be jealous of anyone.

5. UNITY IS STRENGTH

Once, a flock of parrots got caught in the trap laid by the birdcatcher. The birds were in a panic. They tried to free themselves, but couldn't do so. One of the birds then calmed herself and turned towards her friends, saying, "Friends, let's not panic. On the count of three, we will fly together and take this net with us. That is how we will escape this trap." So the wise parrot did a count to three, and on that, all the parrots flapped their wings together and flew. Seeing their wisdom and unity, the birdcatcher was in deep shock!

Moral: If you are working in unity, you can do anything.

6. THE STORY OF TWO CATS

A thin cat asked a fat cat from where did he get food. "I go to the palace to eat a lot of food, without anyone noticing me," the fat cat explained. "Wow! Will you take me too? the thin cat requested. So the fat cat agreed and took him. Just that day, the King had ordered his guards to catch any cat that tries to steal the palace food. Before entering the palace, the cats heard about the King's order. "We should leave. It's not nice to be caught by guards," the fat cat said. But the thin cat was too determined to eat the palace food and went ahead. In doing so, he was caught by the King's guard and thrown in the little prison for animals!

Moral: We must stay happy with what we already have.

7. THE ELEPHANTS AND THE KING OF MICE

A group of mice marched to the Elephant King and said, "We would like to tell you that we have a king of our own. We don't need you as our King." The king elephant said to the mice, "That's not possible. I have already been made the King of this jungle, and you have to obey my orders. Otherwise, you will have to leave this jungle." The mice made a plan. They said to the elephants, "Whoever will prove to be stronger, will be the king of this jungle." So, they all agreed. The next day, all the elephants came. The king mice said, "If you can dig small holes as we did, then you win." The elephants said, "And if you can lift this big log, then you win." Indeed, the elephants won as the mice were not as strong as the elephants.

Moral: Never think yourself to be better than others.

8. THE TRUTHFUL DEER

A hunter was searching for an animal to hunt when he spotted a deer and shot an arrow at it. Surprised to see the arrow, the deer requested the hunter saying, "Sir, please don't kill me yet. Let me meet my family once before I die." The hunter did not believe the deer, so he followed him to his home. On reaching, the deer told his family about the hunter. The deer family turned towards the hunter, saying, "We are a family who cannot live without each other. Please kill us too." Seeing their love as a family, the hunter let them go free and promised never to kill any animal again.

Moral: Pure hearted will always find a place in heaven.

9. THE LION AND THE BEAR

Once a lion and a bear were fighting over a deer they had caught. "It is mine," the lion argued. "No! It is mine," the bear said back. Neither wanted to share their catch. At this, a fight broke out between them. Soon, they were tired and lay down. There was a fox who had been watching. He dodged them and took the deer. He ran away from there. The lion and the bear were shocked. They thought that if they had shared their prey in a friendly way, they both could have had a good meal. But now they had nothing, while the fox was eating a good meal!

Moral: Sharing shows how much we care.

10. THE FOX AND THE TURTLE

A fox caught a turtle and tried to eat it. but could not bite through its shell. "What is up with this shell?" he shouted in frustration. The turtle was smart and thought of a way to escape. He peeped out his head a little from his shell and said, "Put me in the water. That will soften my shell." The foolish fox listened to the turtle and immediately put it in the water. As soon as the turtle landed on the surface of the water, he escaped to a faraway distance and shouted, "Thanks to your foolishness, now I am safe, and you are hungry!"

Moral: Sometimes, being calm can help us think of better solutions to our problems.

11. THE BEAR AND THE BEES

A hungry bear was searching for some food. He found a honeycomb dripping with honey. As soon as the bear tried to take a big scoop of honey out of it, a bee stung him sharply. "Ouch!" the bear shouted at the top of his voice as he jumped in the air with pain. This made the bear very angry. So he swatted at the honeycomb with all his might. But the sudden attack of the bear made the entire swarm of bees come after him in full rage. All the bees started to sting the bear one by one. Crying in pain, the poor bear ran out of the place and never returned.

Moral: Treat people the way you want to be treated.

12. THE SNAKE AND THE EAGLE

Once, an eagle was flying high up in the sky. He saw a snake in a beautiful garden below. The eagle asked "You look sad. What are you doing in this beautiful garden?" The snake looked up at the eagle and said, "Sometimes I wish to go to some other place. I'm tired of staying in one place." The eagle said, "That's not a problem. I can take you to faraway places. This way you can see other beautiful gardens too." The snake was very happy and asked the eagle to take him to another place.

Moral: Be kind to others. Always be willing to help.

13. THE BLUEBIRD AND THE COYOTE

A coyote saw a bluebird and asked him, "You are so blue and beautiful. What is your secret?" "If you bathe in the Rivera Lake four times every morning, for four days and pray, the lake will turn your skin blue and beautiful," the bluebird replied. Every day for four days straight, the coyote bathed in the water of the lake and prayed. The coyote was very proud of himself but kept turning back to see if his shadow was blue too. While doing so, he banged into a tree and fell into a big pile of dust. His colour changed to dusty-brown. Since then all the coyotes have the colour of the dusty earth.

Moral: Be careful when you are walking.

14. THE STAG AND THE LION

One day, a lion saw a stag and started running after him. The stag ran for his life to quite some distance. While running, the stag tripped and got his antlers stuck in a thick branch of a huge tree. He tried hard but could not free himself. He was trapped! Then, he realised, "I was wrong to think less about my legs and hoofs, which helped me to run fast. I had been so proud of my huge antlers that brought me near to my end."

Moral: We should never be too proud of anything.

15. THE CLEVER HARE

In a jungle, all animals had to send one animal to a lion for his food. It was the hare's turn to go to the lion. On reaching the place where the lion lay in wait, the hare pretended to breathe heavily. "Why are you breathing heavily? Your home is nearby, you didn't have to run," asked the lion. "Oh Sir, I just escaped another lion on the way. He called himself the King of the jungle and wanted to eat me. So I ran and came to you," the hare said. "What? Another lion? And he dares call himself the King," the lion said in anger. "Take me to him!" the lion ordered. So the hare brought the lion to a well. "He is down there, look," the hare said, pointing inside the well. The lion peeped and saw his reflection. But the foolish lion thought it was another lion. In anger, he jumped inside the water to attack but ended up drowning. The cunning hare saved all the animals from the cruel lion.

Moral: Being intelligent is better than being strong.

16. THE STORK IN THE HEN HOUSE

A stork was flying high in the sky when he suddenly crashed into a hen house. The house was filled with a turkey and a few hens. They were shocked to see the stork and found him to be a weird-looking bird. The turkey was proud of his looks. So he started to show-off in front of the stork. He also began to make fun of the stork. "Oh my, you have funny legs. They are so long and thin." But the stork ignored his insults and became friends with the hens. The turkey wasn't happy to see the stork be friendly with the hens. He suddenly started to jump up and down. This broke the hen house which scared the stork, and he flew away. The farmer heard the noise and came to see what was happening. He got very angry to see the bird go away and gave the turkey a good spanking.

Moral: Ignore insults. You are a wonderful person, no matter what others say.

17. THE FLY AND THE ANT

One day, a fly and an ant were fighting to know who lives the right way. The fly said many things that were horrible to the ant. "You are so weird and of no use. Look at me. I am the daughter of the air! I can go to palaces and sit on the plates of the kings. After around, I can still walk out on the King's crown!" The ant was listening to the fly patiently. After taking a big sigh, the ant replied, "Well, it's true that you can fly in the air, but it makes no difference whether you sit on the King's crown or a donkey's. Even a small breeze of air can make you fall hard to the ground. Learn to be humble and respect everyone."

Moral: Learn to be humble and respect everyone.

18. THE FOX AND THE ROOSTER

Once a clever fox went confidently to the rooster, who saw him and ran on top of a small hut. The clever fox said sweet words to the rooster about his bright coloured feathers and asked him to sing his sweet cock-a-doodle-doo! The rooster felt proud of his voice. He began to say 'cock-a-doodle-doo', but was just then caught by the fox in his mouth! The fox started running with the rooster when some people saw this act and ran after him. The smart rooster said, "These silly people are calling me 'their rooster'. But I now belong to you." The fox opened his mouth to agree and say, "Yes" and the rooster flew to safety!

Moral: The right things are done at the right time.

19. THE BIRDS AND THE MONKEY

Under a huge tree, some monkeys were taking shelter from the rain. The birds on the tree saw the monkeys standing under the shade of the tree. Seeing their sad faces, the bird felt pity for them. They told the monkeys, "Why don't you make shelter like us on the trees that can protect you." The monkeys thought the birds were making fun of them. Filled with anger, they tried to harm the birds and destroy their nests. But the birds quickly flew to the top of the tree. Seeing their behaviour, the birds asked, "We tried to help you, but you took it as an insult. Is this how you repay someone's kindness?" Hearing their questions, the monkeys immediately apologised to the birds.

Moral: We must learn to appreciate someone's act of kindness.

20. THE FOX WITH THE STUNTED TAIL

A fox had a bad habit of losing his tail. "Why am I the only one without a tail? Wait, let me convince other foxes to lose their tails as well. In that way, I will not be an odd one out," he thought to himself. When he tried to convince others to lose their tails, the other foxes replied, "You are only saying this because you have lost your tail. Had you not lost your tail, you would praise these beautiful tails." fox with the stunted tail ran away in shame.

Moral: Be happy with what you have.

21. THE KING OF THE FOREST GOES TO WAR

Before going to the war, all animals came to the Lion King. "Sir, the donkey is a foolish animal and the rabbit is frightened easily among all," one of the animals said to the King.

The lion turned to his animals and said, "The donkey will dress up as my minister and act as the trumpeter because of his braying voice. The rabbit will become my messenger as he can run the fastest. Learn to see good in everyone."

Moral: Every person is special and unique.

22. THE FOX AND THE GOAT

A thirsty fox reached a well with some water below. The fox quickly jumped into the bucket at the top. His weight made the bucket go down, and he drank the water. Sometime later, a goat was passing by. The fox told her, "If you want to drink water, you should get into the bucket on top. When you come down, I would go up." "But how will I get back?" the goat asked. He replied, "I can come down, and you will go up." The goat agreed. The fox reached the top. The goat cried out, "You promised to help me to come up!" The clever fox replied, "I did not make a promise; we only discussed possibilities,' and quickly left.

Moral: Don't be a fool to trust anyone blindly.

23. THE WOLF AND THE SHEPHERD

A shepherd left his sheep with a wolf, thinking, "Maybe the wolf is a friend instead of an enemy!" One day, the shepherd went to the city for some work. He left his flock in the wolf's care. When he returned in the evening, the poor shepherd found that all his sheep had been taken away by the wolf. Seeing this, the shepherd realised that it was entirely his fault, as he had been foolish enough to trust an enemy.

Moral: Never put blind trust in anyone.

24. THE BELL ON THE CAT

A group of mice gathered to discuss, Why do we have to live in the holes of the houses? they asked each other. "This is all because of the cats. They have killed many of our friends." "We must do something about it," said one of the mice. "Why don't we put a bell around the neck of a cat," said a couple. Everyone agreed to the idea and found it to be perfect. But no one dared to do so, and remain to live in the holes of the houses.

Moral: Have the courage to do what is right.

25. THE MARK OF WISDOM

A rabbit went to a witch to help him get intelligent. She said, "Get me a living python, and I will give you wisdom." The rabbit came up with an idea. He took a long branch and called out to the python, saying, "I bet you are smaller in height than this branch." Challenged, the python stretched itself on the branch. Immediately, the rabbit tied the python on the branch and gave it to the witch. On receiving, she then asked the rabbit to get her a swarm of bees as the second test. The rabbit went to a beehive with a pumpkin in his hand. He made a small hole in the pumpkin and filled it with honey. This attracted the bees, and the rabbit sealed them in the pumpkin. The witch was pleased and gave the rabbit the wisdom in the form of a white spot on its tail, which became the mark of wisdom!

Moral: Seek wisdom more than riches; you will be happier.

26. THE CAMEL AND THE JACKAL

One day, George, the camel, and Henry, the jackal saw some sugarcane fields across the river. They crossed the river, with Henry sitting on George's back. Having had his fill of the sweet sugarcanes, Henry wanted to sing aloud. George told him, "Don't you dare think about singing, or the farmer will see what we have done and beat me because I have not finished eating yet!" But Henry started to shout. Hearing him, the farmers came and started beating George, as he had feared. When George ran to the bank of the river, Henry acted to be sorry for him. George decided to teach him a lesson. On their way back, he said, "I want to lie down in the water!" Henry got scared, but George lay down in the river, with Henry floating away in the water.

Moral: As you sow, so shall you reap.

27. THE WOLF AND THE LAMB

A wolf spotted a lamb drinking water from a stream. He shouted at the lamb, "Why are you making my part of the stream dirty?" The little lamb was not someone who could be fooled easily. He said, "How is that possible? You are standing at a higher height than me, and the water does not flow up, it flows down!" The wolf tried again, "I think you are the same lamb who insulted my father last year." The lamb got angry and said, "I was not even born then!" In frustration, the wolf jumped to attack the little lamb. But he slipped in the water and flew away with the stream!

Moral: It isn't easy to reason with a person who isn't ready to listen to you.

28. THE FOX AND THE CROW

Seeing a crow eat a piece of cheese, a hungry fox also desired to eat it. He quickly thought of a plan. The fox said to the crow, "My friend, you have such a beautiful voice. I have not heard you singing for so long. Please, can you sing a song for me? I will listen to your song then go away." The crow was very pleased. As soon as he opened his mouth to sing, the juicy piece of cheese fell. The fox picked it up and said to the crow, "Thank you, my friend. Now I can enjoy this cheese."

Moral: Think before believing those who try to fool you.

29. THE FAITHFUL HORSE AND THE FOX

A farmer commanded his old horse to get a lion. On his way, while the horse was lost in thoughts, he found a sly fox, and his witty nature made him a fast friend of the horse. "Don't worry, my friend. I have an idea. Just lie still in the middle of the road, and the lion will be yours," the fox said. As the horse lay still in the middle of the road, a lion came strolling by and stopped to look at the horse carefully. As soon as the lion came close to the horse, the fox tied their tails, and shouted, "Run horse, run!" Dragging the lion with him, the horse brought the lion to the farmer. And so he fulfilled the farmer's wish, living on the farm for the rest of his life.

Moral: Work hard, and you will receive your reward.

30. THE LION AND HIS PARTNERS

A company of a lion, a sheep, a goat, and a cow decided they would always share everything equally. One bright summer day, they caught a deer and held a meeting to determine how to divide it amongst themselves. The lion asked about making four equal parts. He declared, "As it's my right, the first share will be mine. Since I happen to be the King of the Forest, I will also take the second share. And since I am the strongest, I will take the third share too. If you claim the rest, I will throw you out of the forest." The animals were puzzled to hear what the lion said, and realised they got tricked.

Moral: Always fulfil the promises you make with people.

31. THE FOX AND THE MONKEY KING

In a jungle, all the animals wanted to make a monkey as their King. They said, "Yes! We have chosen you to be the King because you make us all happy by showing your funny tricks." Among the animals, there was a fox too. One day, he planned to set a trap for the monkey. He hid the trap under some leaves and placed a banana over them. Then, he invited the monkey and said, "Dear King, this banana is for you. Please take it." As soon as the monkey stepped forward to pick up that banana, he got trapped. The fox laughed at the monkey and said, "You are not very smart to be a king. If you can't save yourself, how will you take care of this animal kingdom?"

Moral: When others do well, don't be jealous of them.

32. THE ROOSTER, THE CAT AND THE MOUSE

One day, a hen laid eggs. When the rooster came to check, he found that one egg was missing. He asked the cat, "Did you take one egg?" The cat said, "No, my friend, I did not." A mouse was passing by when the rooster saw him. He tried to stop the mouse and asked him, "Did you take one egg from here?" The mouse said, "No, I did not." The rooster did not believe the mouse and asked the cat to chase the mouse. The mouse was scared of the cat and started to run. Just then, the mother hen came out and told the rooster that one egg had broken, so she had thrown the shells away. Soon, the mouse was gone and never returned to that place.

Moral: Don't blame anyone without knowing the truth.

33. THE OWL AND THE SEAGULL

The owl and the seagull were great friends for quite some time. One day, the owl was not able to fly. Although he was used to sleeping at night, he was not able to sleep at all. He had also not eaten anything. The seagull said, "Dear friend, I can see that you have not eaten anything at all. I will go and get you something to eat." The owl was very thankful for the seagull. Soon, the seagull returned with something to eat for the owl. The owl was well again.

Moral: Always help your friends in need.

34. THE CAT AND THE OLD MOUSE

A cat did not really like that old mouse and wanted to get rid of it one day. The old mouse gathered all the other mice to discuss the cat's plan. He turned to them and said, "We will scare the cat away so that it would never think of chasing us away." Everyone agreed. They invited the cat for dinner one evening. After eating all that was served, the cat pretended to be sick. He laid down, pretending as if he is dead. But the intelligent mice knew that the cat is only acting. So they brought a large sack of flour and poured it all on the cat. Just as the flour went inside the cat's nose, he sneezed so hard that he got up and ran away and never came close to any mice.

Moral: Never try to cheat anyone.

35. THE CAT AND THE CROW

It was a bright, sunny day. The cat and the crow were playing and enjoying their time when they heard a roar! It was a leopard. It was coming near them. At once, the crow flew up in the branches of a tall tree, but the poor cat could not run anywhere as it had hurt its foot. The crow quickly went in search of some help. He saw a shepherd who had some dogs. He said to the dogs, "Please come quickly. My friend is in trouble." The dogs quickly ran and followed the crow. The dogs were barking very loudly, and the leopard heard them and ran away. Thus, the crow was able to save his friend's life.

Moral: A friend in need is a friend indeed.

36. THE WEASELS AND THE MICE

One day, mice came to the weasels and said, "We have heard that some other animals are going to come here and destroy our houses. We must do something together." The weasels agreed. The father weasel said, "We will mark our area and this way no one will enter our area." The father mice said, "That's an excellent idea!" So, they all brought flags with which they would mark their area and not allow anyone else inside. The father mice also brought with him a spear. He said, "I have brought this spear so that in case anyone tries to force and enter our area, I can stop them." Happily, they all put flags around their area, which did not allow anyone else to enter. They all then lived peacefully.

Moral: Work together as a team.

37. THE FOX AND THE GRAPES

A fox once reached a vineyard and found some juicy looking grapes hanging from the branches. He tried jumping "hop! hop" to grab some grapes, but he could not. He kept trying many times, but each time he failed. By now, he was too tired to try anymore. Since he was so hungry, he didn't have any more strength to jump. So, he said to himself, "These branches are too high. I can't reach them. I think these grapes are not good enough to be eaten. They don't even look sweet." Then he left the place without trying any further.

Moral: Try, try, at last, you will succeed.

38. THE LION AND THE DONKEY

One day, a lion asked his friend donkey, "Would you like to come along with me for hunting?" The donkey was very happy and said, "Of course, I would love to come." The lion dressed him with leaves. The donkey didn't know why the lion had covered him with leaves. The lion wanted to fool other animals. Some small deer were playing around. While they were busy playing, the donkey brayed loudly, "Hee-Haw! Hee-Haw!" The deer got so scared that they ran away very fast to their home. The lion was angry at his friend donkey and said that he would never ask the donkey to come with him. But the donkey felt sorry for the little deer and told the lion that he should not think of harming such animals.

Moral: You must have a love for all animals. Never harm them in any way.

39. THE CUP WINNERS

In a race, the first prize was given to the hare, but the snail was given the second prize. The snail asked the sunflower, who was one of the judges, "Why did you give me second prize?" The sunflower said, "The prize goes to the one with more strength and patience." But, the snail was still not very happy. The lamp post said to the snail, "Each year, prizes are given according to the alphabetical order. So, this year, the prize goes to the one with the name starting with the letter 'H'. Next year, those whose names begin with 'I' will be given the prize." Now the snail was happy with the reason why the hare got the first prize instead of him and went away.

Moral: Be fair in everything that you do.

40. THE DOG AND THE DONKEY

A dog once said to the donkey, "I am quite tired of keeping awake throughout the night and guarding. I want to get some sleep. Would you please keep watch for me while I sleep?" The donkey said, "Sure, my friend. I can do that. You go to sleep while I'll keep a watch." The dog told the donkey that, if he sees thieves coming, he should bray loudly and chase away the thieves. The dog went to sleep. The donkey was keeping a close watch. Suddenly, he saw some thieves coming near the house. He began to bray loudly. "HEE-HAW! HEE-HAW!" The dog also woke up and began to bark. The thieves didn't come any closer and ran away.

Moral: You must be helpful to each other.

41. THE FOX AND THE WOLF IN COURT

A fox and a wolf were fighting to know who was a cheater among them. The fox and the wolf came to the monkey and said, "Since you are our judge. Tell us, who is wrong?" The monkey who was quite clever went down the tree. He said to them, "I think the wolf is wrong by speaking lies about the fox. And you fox, are also wrong since you are very cunning by nature. So, I think both of you need to be sent to prison." The fox and the wolf decided that it was better to become friends and live peacefully.

Moral: Act wisely. It is better to live peacefully than quarrel with others.

42. THE SILLY WOLF AND THE BILLY GOAT

One day, an old wolf was chasing a billy goat. The goat jumped to a high rock. From there it shouted, "Why are you chasing me? Just open your mouth, and I'll jump in." The silly wolf listened to the goat and opened his mouth. In doing so, the goat jumped, but landed on the wolf's face and ran away. When the wolf woke up, he noticed his mouth was still open. He forgot if he had eaten to billy goat or not. Since he couldn't come up with an answer, he left an empty stomach.

Moral: Smartness can help you in any situation.

43. THE HARE AND THE FROGS

One day, a hare was walking near a pond, when he saw some frogs playing in the water. He said to the frogs, "You all are so brave. Are you not afraid of anyone?" Just then, they all heard a loud noise near the pond. The frogs quickly went into the water and hid. The hare also promptly ran and hid in a hole. The hare then realised that he was not the only one who was so timid.

Moral: Don't think yourself less than others.

44. THE MONKEY AND THE CROCODILE

Once a crocodile took some jambolan fruit for his wife, given by his friend monkey. She asked the crocodile, "How sweet these fruits are! I'm sure monkey's heart would taste sweet too. Why don't you call him home for dinner?" The next day, the crocodile said to the monkey, "My wife enjoyed the sweet fruits you gave. She has invited you to a grand dinner tonight. I will take you on my back." The monkey was pleased and jumped quickly and sat on the crocodile's back. When they were on their way, the crocodile told the monkey that his wife was sick and it's only the monkey's heart that can save her. The monkey quickly said, "Oh! Why didn't you tell me before? I've left my heart on that tree. We'll have to go back." The foolish crocodile took the monkey back, and the clever monkey quickly climbed on the tree and saved his life.

Moral: Never try to cheat your good friends.

45. THE LION AND THE BADGER

In a jungle, a fox and a badger were walking by, and they saw a lion was standing in front of the poor sheep. They thought that the lion is trying to harm the sheep. The fox said to the lion "Why are you scaring that poor creature. Let him go." The lion said, "No, my friend, I'm only nice to him." The sheep saw that the lion was not doing anything, and he too made friends with the lion. Then they all lived happily together as friends.

Moral: Don't judge anyone by seeing their outward look. People are kind from their heart.

46. THE FOX AND THE STORK

A fox once invited a stork for dinner at his house. When the stork came for dinner, the fox gave him food in a flat plate. The stork could not eat at all from the plate. He also thought of doing the same to the fox. The next day, the stork invited the fox for dinner. The stork served food in two jugs with narrow necks. Because of the jug's narrow neck, the fox failed to taste the soup. But the stork sipped it with ease. The fox lost his temper, the Stork said calmly, "The way you will treat others, you too will be treated in the same way." The fox realised that he was paid for his mischief.

Moral: Treat others the way you would want to be treated.

47. THE DONKEY AND THE GRASSHOPPER

A donkey saw some grasshoppers and asked them, "How come you have such a sweet voice? What do you eat?" The grasshopper said to the donkey, "We eat grass early in the morning. This helps us in singing too." The next day the donkey too began to eat grass in the morning. But his voice never changed. So, he went and asked the grasshopper, "You said that you eat grass in the morning; that's why you can sing so beautifully. I also ate the same grass, but my voice didn't change at all." The grasshopper told the donkey that it is not the grass but that their voice has always been that way. The donkey understood and went away with a sad face.

Moral: Be happy with what you have.

48. THE MOUSE PRINCESS

A witch once changed a queen's child into a mouse. The witch told the queen, "Now the princess will only change when she laughs." Many years passed. A prince invited everyone to his castle for a dance. All the other daughters of the King went except the mouse. When they all left, the mouse tied a ribbon to the rooster's beak and sat on it. She reached the prince's palace, where everyone was dancing. When she saw the witch's sister dancing, she laughed so loudly that she turned back into a beautiful princess. When the prince saw her, he asked her to marry her.

Moral: Don't be jealous of others. Do good to them.

49. BONDO, THE WOLF, AND THE STRAY DOG

Bondo, the wolf, was searching for food when he saw a thin-looking stray dog. He called out to the dog. Where are you going?" The stray dog said, "I am looking for a treasure which I had hidden some days back in this jungle." Bondo was thrilled, but he also wanted to eat the dog. The dog said to him, "You may eat me only after you help me search the treasure." Bondo agreed and helped in digging to find the hidden treasure. When they both finished digging quite deep, the dog said to Bondo, "Whoever will jump first will get the treasure I've hidden." Without thinking, Bondo jumped into the pit. He looked everywhere but didn't find anything. The stray dog laughed and went away.

Moral: Think before you speak. Look before you leap.

50. THE TWO ROOSTERS AND THE EAGLE

One day, two roosters were fighting very loudly. While they were fighting, one of them became the winner. He said, "Since I won, so I am the master of this farm. Now you will have to obey all my orders!" The winner happily crowed and clapped its wings! He became so proud that he did not even see an eagle flying above in the sky. The eagle heard the noise and came down. Quickly he took away the winner. He screamed, but nobody could help him. Now, the farm belonged to the defeated rooster!

Moral: Never fight over something. Share what you have with others too.

51. THE MONKEYS AND THE BELL

One day, some monkeys found a bell and began ringing it. They made such a long, continuous noise that everybody started noticing the sound. All the villagers were afraid and thought, "It must be a giant who is making this scary noise!" Only one woman was not scared. She took a basket of fruits to where she'd heard the bell ringing. She put down the fruit basket on the ground and hid behind a tree. As soon as the monkeys jumped on the fruits, she picked up the bell and rushed back. All the villagers were happy.

Moral: Always be courageous.

52. THE OX AND THE HORSE

A horse and an ox had a master who was in the army. The horse said, "I am worried about the dangers our master would have to face during the war." On the other hand, the ox was very cheerful and said, "If our master were not here, we would have very little to do!" But the master's plan changed as soon as the news reached about the enemy who was not attacking them anymore. In celebration of this news, the cavalryman hosted a big banquet where roast meat was plenty! Do you know who the loser was?

Moral: Always be faithful and loyal to your friends and loved ones.

53. THE EAGLE AND THE BADGER

Once, a cat went up to the eagle and told him, "The badger is digging through the roots so that the tree falls and with it, your babies, which he will then eat!" She then climbed down and told the badger, "Don't ever leave your home! That eagle above you is just waiting for you and your little ones to leave the house so that he can eat you all up." Both the eagle and the badger did not go to look for food for a few days. When their children were hungry, they realised that they had been tricked. The angry eagle and badger then became friends and never believed the cat again.

Moral: Never put blind faith in anyone.

54. THE MONKEY AND THE DOLPHIN

A terrible sea storm hit a ship, and everyone fell into the sea. All of them drowned. A dolphin was passing by and saw the monkey drowning. She thought, "I must help the poor creature." She picked him up. She felt that "I will take him to the seashore on my back." When they reached near an island, the dolphin asked the monkey, "Do you know this place?" The monkey showed off and said "Yes. The emperor of this island and I are best friends!" The dolphin knew that no one lived on that island. She got angry and shook the monkey off her back for telling a lie.

Moral: You should never lie to anyone.

55. THE SICK LION

A zebra came to visit the sick Lion King. On getting close, he said, "Your Majesty! You have a bad breath" This made the lion angry, and he ordered him to leave the forest. The hyena saw all this and got scared. He remarked over the pleasant smell all around. The lion said, "I am not stupid!" He asked him to leave the forest. Finally, the lion went to the clever fox for his thoughts. The fox saved himself by saying, "My nose is blocked due to cold, and so I cannot smell a thing!"

Moral: Be smart enough to get out of a situation.

56. THE SNAKE AND THE ANTS

A long time ago, there was a poisonous snake. All the tiny creatures living around were scared of him. Proudly, he thought to himself, "I am the most powerful of all. Everybody is scared of me. One day, he saw an anthill near the hole in which he lived. He was outraged. He decided to destroy the ugly anthill and attacked it. As he was about to attack the anthill, one of the ants saw him. He quickly went inside and warned everybody. Within moments, thousands of ants came out and bit the snake all over his body. The snake couldn't bear the pain and died soon after that.

Moral: Pride takes you to a fall.

57. THE WOLF AND THE GOAT

A small goat got separated from his flock and lost his way. Soon, he met a wolf who offered, "Would you like to walk with me home?" The goat said, "Thanks! But I think I can manage by myself." The wolf said that he was worried that a wicked animal might hurt the goat. The goat observed that he did not think anybody else would hurt him, except the wolf! The wolf said that rather than the goat being hurt by somebody else, he would instead pack him inside his tummy! And he jumped on the goat. The goat attacked in return and ran away.

Moral: Be careful in all situations.

58. THE PEACOCK AND THE CRANE

A proud peacock would often taunt everyone by saying, "My feathers are covered in gold and purple, while you have very plain and boring wings." The crane felt terrible about it. But one day, he thought of giving the peacock a good answer. He said, "I could sing to the stars as I flew high in the sky, but you have to drag yourself on the ground, as low as the chickens did in their farmyard!" The peacock was shocked and realised that he also had flaws like the others.

Moral: Everybody is unique in their ways.

59. THE PIGEON AND THE ANT

A pigeon spotted a drowning ant and decided to help it. He put down the leaf near the ant, and she climbed on to it. The pigeon carried it and set down the ant safely on the stream's bank. They became friends. Some days later, the ant was resting when she saw a hunter. Just then, the pigeon flew into his nest. The hunter saw the pigeon and aimed at it. The ant immediately went and bit the hunter hard on his leg. The hunter jumped in pain and missed the pigeon. The ant had saved her friend's life.

Moral: A friend in need is a friend indeed.

60. THE DONKEY WHO SANG A SONG

Two friends, a donkey and a jackal, were enjoying some juicy tomatoes. The donkey was very happy and said, "I feel like singing." The jackal warned him, "Please, don't make any noise. The owner of the field will hear you and will come running with sticks." But the donkey did not pay any attention to the jackal's advice and began to sing loudly. The jackal left after realising the danger that would come. He hid behind a nearby bush. The owner heard the loud singing. He ran to the spot with a heavy stick in his hand. He beat the donkey so hard that the donkey forgot to sing and cried in pain.

Moral: Listen to the good advice given by friends.

61. THE DECEITFUL CRANE

One day, all the animals were tricked by a crane who said their lake was about to dry up. The crane said, "If you want, I can carry you to another lake far away." Everybody thanked him. The wicked crane took two fishes each day and filled its stomach. One day, it decided to eat a crab. The crab saw a lot of fish skeletons on the rocks below and understood the cunning crane's plan. He acted quickly and used his claws to kill the crane and save his life. On returning to the lake, he told everyone about the crane's wickedness.

Moral: Even in the most dangerous situations, you can always rely on your intelligence and cleverness to save you.

62. WHY THE BEAR IS STUMPY-TAILED

On seeing a fox catch a fish, a bear asked, "How did you catch the fish?" The fox said, "It's simple. First, you need to make a hole in the ice and then stick your tail inside. The fish will come to bite it and get stuck to it." The bear did that. But the ice closed around his tail, and he was stuck. He tried hard and pulled himself away, but most of his tail was left behind. It never grew back again!

Moral: You should not always believe everything you are told.

63. THE GOAT AND THE DONKEY

A goat was always very jealous of a donkey, as she was always tied up. Cleverly, she praised the donkey for the hard work he did. She told him, "Why don't you pretend to have a broken leg so that you can get some rest?" The silly donkey agreed, but he really broke his leg! The doctor told the master, "The donkey should be fed goat soup." The kind master decided to save his donkey by killing his goat. As he went to her with a knife, the goat realised her mistake and ran for her life.

Moral: We should never give ill-advice to anyone.

64. THE LION AND THE GRATEFUL MOUSE

A hungry lion caught a mouse. Just as he was about to eat it, the mouse requested, "Please let me be free, and I will help you one day." The lion king roared with laughter at this stupidity, but let the mouse go. Some days later, some hunters were passing by, and they saw a huge lion. They decided to catch him. The lion got trapped in a net which the hunters had set. As the lion lay there feeling helpless, the grateful mouse came and cut through the net with his small but sharp teeth. Slowly, the lion was free. "Now you know how even the weak can help the mighty," the mouse told the lion.

Moral: The weak can help the mighty.

65. THE CROW AND THE SWAN

One day a crow asked a swan, What are the secret of your beauty and white feathers?" The swan replied, "I am white and beautiful because I live in water all the time." On hearing this, the crow jumped into the pond. After some time, he felt as if his body was going to freeze. After some difficulty, he came out of the pond. He was feeling freezing and was still as black as ever! The swan was surprised. So, he mocked at him, "Are you afraid of water? I never thought you would give up so soon." The crow had no answer to this. He thought to himself, "Crows are not meant to live in water. I was a fool to have even tried to do so."

Moral: Never do something that is not meant for you.

66. THE WICKED SNAKE

An evil snake always used to break the eggs of a crow couple. One day the crows decided, "Let's make a plan to teach the evil snake a lesson!" The next morning, the female crow picked up a necklace of a princess from the palace and flew away. Seeing this, the royal guards chased the crow. The crow dropped the necklace into the snake's hole, and it came out. When the guards saw the snake, they killed it. Then, they safely took the necklace out of the hole and went back to the princess. The crows were very happy that their plan had worked, and they lived happily ever after.

Moral: Never trouble anyone.

67. THE ELEPHANT AND THE DOG

A royal elephant and a dog were great friends. A farmer met their caretaker once. He wanted to buy the dog, and the caretaker gave it to him. The elephant became sad and stopped eating and drinking. The King sent his wisest minister to look into the matter. When questioned, the caretaker admitted, "The elephant had been very friendly with a dog, which had been taken by someone." The King announced, "Whoever had taken the dog should release him, or pay a heavy fine." The farmer let the dog go. The elephant was thrilled to be united again with his friend, and they both lived happily after that.

Moral: True friendships are always treasured.

68. THE SICK CAMEL

A camel fell sick in a desert. His friends heard of him and said, "We must visit him to see if he needs anything." After travelling for long, they rested for a while, staying back with the unwell camel. They ate the grass growing around. The camel felt very happy to meet his relatives and friends. But, when he had become well again, he looked around for something to eat. He found that his visitors had eaten everything up! The camel was left with no choice but to leave his place and travel through the desert, to search for another oasis.

Moral: Be caring and take care of the sick and weak.

69. THE OWL AND THE NIGHTINGALE

Once upon a time, a man caught a nightingale. An owl used to see the nightingale sing only at night. He was confused and asked the nightingale, "What is the reason for singing only at night?" The nightingale told him, "I was trapped during the day when I was singing. I realised that I should be more careful and began singing only at night." "Are you scared that you may be put in a cage again?" asked the owl. "I think it would have been better for you if you had been more careful the first time. It shouldn't matter anymore to you now!" the owl said.

Moral: Old habits are difficult to change.

70. TRUE, VERY TRUE

One day, a respected hen broke off one of her feathers with her beak. She sighed, "I've broken another feather! I'll never look beautiful!" Her neighbour told the mother hen, "One of my sisters is trying to make herself look beautiful by pulling out all her feathers." The owl, sitting atop the hen house remarked, "Shameless creature!" His wife shouted at him, saying, "Be quiet! The children should not hear this." But she flew off and told the pigeons, "Did you know? One of the hens is in love with the rooster and has plucked out all her feathers!" The pigeons told this story, but it was about two featherless hens! On hearing this, the first hen, who had no idea that this had started because of her, exclaimed, "What a scene! These hens should be ashamed of themselves."

Moral: Everybody is beautiful in their way.

71. THE TWO GOATS

Once two goats were best friends, and all the jungle animals were jealous of their friendship. One day, the animals cleverly asked one goat to go to one side of the river for grazing and sent the other goat to the other side. At sunset, the animals asked one goat to return. As it started, the animals, on the other end, asked the other goat to return. They were all sure that the goats would lock horns in the middle. But the goats thought, "One goat should lay down on the bridge, while the other jump over it!" Soon, both reached to their right places!

Moral: Being wise can solve your problems quickly.

72. THE BEES AND THE HORNETS GO TO COURT

One day, the bees and the hornets fought over a honeycomb. The judge was a wasp, and he was unable to decide who the rightful owners were. Witnesses said, "The black and yellow insects had been seen going in and out of the honeycomb." But this did not help, as both bees and hornets have black and yellow bodies! The Queen Bee told the judge, "Why don't you let the bees and hornets make another honeycomb? Whichever group builds the best comb in the shortest time can be declared the owner of that comb." The hornets do not know how to build honeycombs, so they disagreed with this idea. The wasp understood that the honey and honeycomb could only rightfully belong to the bees!

Moral: Never claim for anything that does not belong to you.

73. THE FAR-SIGHTED SWAN

One day, an old, wise swan saw a small twiner growing near the tree. He warned the others, "This twiner may be dangerous for us." But nobody took it seriously. A birdcatcher came to that tree and climbed up with the help of the same twiner. He set a net to catch the swans and came down. As soon as the swans flew to their nests, they all got trapped! They all cried, "Help!" Soon, the wise swan came up with a plan. As the birdcatcher came, he saw them lying motionless. He thought, "I think they all are dead!" He dropped them on to the ground. At once, they all flew away!

Moral: Unity is the best remedy.

74. THE HARE AND THE TORTOISE

One day, a hare challenged the slow tortoise to a race to which the tortoise agreed. Reaching a field, The hare ate some vegetables and fruits. There was no sign of the tortoise, so he decided to rest. Meanwhile, the tortoise kept running along slowly and steadily. The hare awoke and did not see the tortoise anywhere. But on reaching the finishing point, he saw the tortoise was already there. He was surprised and thought, "How is this possible? The tortoise is very slow, and I am the fastest of all!" All the animals were cheering for the tortoise!

Moral: Slow and steady wins the race.

75. THE ANT AND THE GRASSHOPPER

A singing grasshopper shouted at some ants, "There is time for the winter season. Come join me!" But the ants continued on their way. Summer passed, and then autumn. The ants kept working, while the grasshopper kept singing.

At last, it was winter, and it became freezing. When the grasshopper searched for food, he only found some dry leaves. The grasshopper was starving. He saw an ant going towards its hole. He requested her to give her some of the grain they had stored. The ant disagreed and said, "You were singing while we were working hard. Now you can dance the winter away!"

Moral: Always work hard to save your future.

76. THE SWAN AND THE GOOSE

The two birds swam in a lake happily for weeks. Their master and his guests often came by to admire them and fed them tasty food. Finally, the master told the cook, "Serve me the goose's roasted flesh at dinnertime today." The cook was very drunk. He got confused. He, by mistake, took the swan instead of the goose! When he was about to cook the swan, it began to sing! The surprised cook then didn't think of killing the bird!

Moral: You should be very careful about the work you are doing.

77. THE MUSICIANS OF BREMEN

A donkey and a dog made a plan one day, "Let's go to the city of Bremen and join a choir!" Soon, a cat and a rooster joined them. At night, they found a well-lit hut in the forest. Four thieves lived here. The animals peeped in through the window and saw a delicious meal. They all were hungry so they planned to get it. The dog climbed on top of the donkey, the cat climbed on the dog, and the rooster went right to the top. Together they screamed. The thieves thought there was a big monster and they ran away! Happily, the four animals rushed inside and ate up all the food!

Moral: Together you can get share and spread love.

78. REYNARD THE FOX AND THE FISHES

Reynard, the fox, saw a cart full of fishes and plotted a way of getting a rich meal. Lying down in the centre of the road, he pretended to be dead. The fisherman saw the fox lying on the road. He thought to himself, "This fox looks well-fed. I can surely use the beautiful fox skin." The fisherman lifted the fox and put him at the back in his cart. As soon as they moved, Reynard released all the fishes into the road behind him. The fisherman did not realise what was happening behind his back. The fox then picked them up and ran off! The poor fisherman lost all his fishes and the fox skin too!

Moral: Never be greedy.

79. THE THIRSTY CROW

A thirsty crow was searching for some water. Suddenly, the crow saw a mud pot that had a little water in it. He thought to himself, "I must drink the water to quench my thirst." The crow realised that the water level was too low for him to drink the water. He looked all around for some time. He saw some small pebbles lying near the mud pot. At once, he got an idea. He thought, "I will pick up the pebbles one by one and drop them into the pot." He did so, and soon the water in the pot started coming up. The crow put out his thirst quickly and flew away.

Moral: If you think right, you can find solutions to the problems.

80. THE ROOSTER AND THE JEWEL

A rooster was searching for some food when he found a jewel. At first, he was thrilled to see the shining jewel. He was amazed at how the jewel shone and glittered But when he hit it, he found it was too hard. He couldn't eat it. Looking at the jewel, he thought, "This gem may be very costly, but to me, a single grain of corn is more useful than all the world's jewels." He thought wisely and kept it on the ground and began searching for his food. A poor man found it and sold it. He lived happily ever after.

Moral: An expensive gem cannot take the place of food.

81. THE VIPER, THE FROGS AND THE WATER SNAKE

A viper said to some water snakes, "The water is mine!" They both decided to settle the matter, once and for all, by a fight. The frogs who were the enemies of the water snake gave their support to the viper. When the day of announcing the winner came, the frogs began croaking, as they couldn't think of anything else to do. The viper won. Later, when the frogs asked the viper for their share, the viper began whistling, leaving the frogs confused. The viper told them, "I'm repaying you in the same manner by which you helped me!"

Moral: Always be fair to everyone.

82. THE LARKS IN THE CORNFIELD

A family of larks lived in a nest in a cornfield. Each day, as the mother lark went in search for food, she told the little larks to stay inside the nest and beware of the farmer. One day, the little larks heard the farmer telling his son, "The corn is ready to be cut. We must call our neighbours to help us to reap this field." The little larks got scared. When their mother returned, she got to know about everything. The mother lark smiled and said, "Don't be afraid." The next evening, when the mother lark came home, the little larks said, "Mother! The farmer came again. He said that he would reap this field tomorrow." Hearing this, she said, "My dear children, now we must leave this field tomorrow before the farmer arrives. When a man says he will do his job himself, he will surely do it."

Moral: Never rush to take decisions.

83. THE BOAR AND THE FOXES

Two foxes spotted a wild boar sharpening his tusks. One of them asked him, "Why are you doing that? There is neither any hunter nor any other danger at the moment." "Yes! True" replied the boar. He continued saying, "But whenever a danger appears, I won't get any time to sharpen my teeth. I have to keep them ready for use all the time. Only then I can stay safe in this forest."

Moral: You should always be ready for anything that can happen in the future.

84. THE FARM ROOSTER AND THE WEATHERVANE

Seeing a weathervane, a proud farmyard rooster puffed his chest and showed off his red crest. He boasted about his loud 'cock-a-doodle-doo' to the hens and little chickens.

One day he said, "Even roosters lay eggs that turned into a dragon, scaring men to death!" The weathervane knew the rooster was telling plain white lies but thinking himself to be superior; he did not even try to copy the rooster. But it is difficult to decide who is more important: the rooster or the weathervane!

Moral: Everyone is unique in their ways.

85. HOW THE GREEDY FOX MET ITS END

A hunter spotted a big, fat donkey one day in a forest. He shot an arrow at it, injuring it seriously. But when the hunter went near the donkey, it kicked him and died. A greedy fox was watching all this. It thought, "Indeed, this is my lucky day! Today, I will feed on a donkey and a man!" The fox went to the donkey first and decided to eat the flesh near its wound. As the fox dug its' teeth in, the sharp tip of the hunter's arrow that had entered the donkey's body, pierced its' throat. As a result, the fox also died.

Moral: We should never be greedy as it gives nothing in return.

86. THE TWO MULES AND THE ROBBERS

Two mules were walking with their masters along the same road when they met and started talking. One mule said to the other, "Where are you going?" The other mule replied, "To the city mate". They became good friends. The banker's mule kept boasting about how rich his master is and how well he treated him. There were some robbers in the jungle. They heard the sound of the clinking coins. At once, all of them thought that the mule was carrying gold coins and other rich jewels. The robbers stole the treasure and oats from the mules. They also rained sticks on the poor animal!

Moral: Never steal and be kind to animals.

87. THE GOLDEN BIRD

A king saw a golden bird and asked, "Please stay in the garden forever. I will name you as the Golden Bird." Every morning, the King fed grains to the golden bird with his hand. The swans became jealous of the golden bird. They thought, "The king does not love us as before!" So, they started attacking the golden bird. They asked the golden bird, "Please leave our place." But the golden bird disagreed. It made the King unhappy and everyone else in the palace. The King ordered his soldiers to kill all the swans. They all flew away and lost their royal home because of their jealousy.

Moral: Never be jealous of anyone.

88. THE DONKEY IN THE TIGER'S SKIN

A donkey found a tiger skin and thought, "If I wear this skin, I shall look like a tiger." He wore it and began walking around. A deer thought him for a tiger, and ran away! The donkey thought, "It would be fun to scare the villagers." Soon all the villagers were scared and hid inside their homes! The donkey was very proud of it and made loud noises. The villagers realised it was not a tiger. The next day, the villagers were waiting together with sticks and stones. When the donkey wearing the tiger's skin came, they beat him up! The donkey began to yell. Realising his mistake, he said sorry to everyone and never troubled anyone again.

Moral: We should never trouble anyone.

89. THE CROWS' CHALLENGE

Two crows got into a contest, "Let's see which one could fly higher while carrying a sack." One crow filled cotton into his sack and was surprised to see the other crow filling his sack with salt, which was heavier. Then, both took flight. The crow with light cotton in his sack flew higher than the other one. But soon, it began to rain. The cotton soaked up the raindrops and grew heavy! It became hard for him to fly. On the other hand, the salt in the second crow's sack dissolved in the rain, and his sack became very light! Now, he flew up higher and won the challenge!

Moral: It is mere folly to think oneself wiser than other.

90. THE EAGLE AND THE WOODCUTTER

A kind-hearted woodcutter once rescued an eagle. Sometime later, the woodcutter had climbed on a steep hill to cuts trees for wood. There he got stuck, and couldn't come down. He sat on a rock, waiting for any help to come. Suddenly the eagle he had rescued came flying down towards him. In another moment, the eagle flew away with his hat. The woodcutter became angry and started to chase the eagle. After some time of chasing, he found the way to get down the hill. "Oh, so this is why you took my hat. You wanted me to run behind you and find this way. Thank you so much, my friend," the woodcutter said to the eagle, who was high above in the sky looking at him.

Moral: Kindness will always get great rewards.

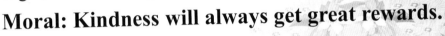

91. THE BIRD CHILD AND THE WITCH

One day a witch was going around in the jungle she saw a bird child and turned it into a beautiful princess. The next day the witch changed herself into an eagle. She flew down to the pond and took that bird child. When the mother of that bird child saw what the eagle had done, she was furious. She said, "Why did you take my child away? Bring her back immediately." The witch said, "No, I want to make her into a beautiful princess." The mother bird disagreed and wanted her child back. But when the bird child was brought back to her mother, it had turned into a beautiful princess. The mother bird was, however, delighted to see her beautiful child.

Moral: Be kind to one another.

92. THE GREEDY DOG

A dog found a juicy bone to eat. On the way, the dog had to cross a bridge built over a small stream. While crossing the bridge, he saw his reflection in the water. Seeing it, he thought that there was another dog with a bone, in the water. "How nice it would be to take that bone away from the other dog!" the greedy dog thought to himself. In wondering so, the dog started barking. The moment he opened his mouth, the bone fell into the water. Thus, the greedy dog did not get any bone and lost his bone too. He felt unfortunate and realised his mistakes.

Moral: Greed brings a feeling of regret.

93. THE LITTLE GOLDFISH

A fisherman once caught a goldfish. Taking pity, he threw it back into the sea, though he knew he could have sold it to a goldsmith and earned a lot of money. "I will reward you for your kindness, but don't say anything to anybody," the goldfish said. When he returned home, he found that his poor hut had become a grand castle, and his wife was wearing an expensive gown. "How have we become so rich?" she asked, and he told her about the goldfish. As he spoke, the castle became their old hut! They were back to being poor, leaving his wife very sad.

Moral: We must follow instructions that are for our good.

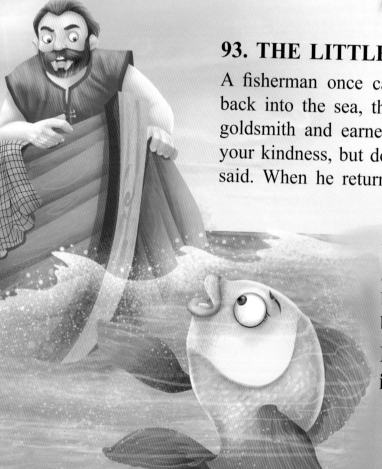

94. THE EAGLE AND THE CROW

A crow was flying above when he saw an eagle jump down on a lamb. The eagle clutched it in its claws and carried it to its nest. The crow was hungry as well. He thought to himself, "I should do the same just like the eagle did to the lamb! This way, I will not starve." The crow started searching for a lamb. He finally spotted a lamb in a garden. The crow tried to do the same as the eagle. There was a shepherd who was passing by. He saw everything that was happening. He quickly caught the crow and locked it in a cage. So, the black crow that tried to mimic the black eagle was laughed at by everybody.

Moral: Never try to copy others.

95. THE FOX AND THE LEOPARD

Once upon a time, there was a fox and a leopard. They had a fight over which of the two was more beautiful. The leopard said, "I am very proud of my glossy spots. You don't even have any of these." He was about to lose his temper when the fox remarked, "You may have glossy spots, but my beauty is not external. I have a sharp mind that makes me more attractive than you." The leopard was shocked as he did not have anything to say to this. He realised that being wise is more important than being beautiful. He left and never troubled the fox again.

Moral: Being wise never lets you fall.

96. THE HUNTER AND THE RABBIT

In an old village, a hunter captured a rabbit. The rabbit said to the hunter, "I will show you a place full of gold to keep you rich for the rest of your life if you let me go." The hunter got very greedy after listening to the deal. He said, "Where is the place? You will have to show it to me now!" The wise rabbit replied, "You first have to leave me, then you can follow me." The moment the hunter placed the rabbit on the ground, the rabbit ran away. The hunter watched the rabbit flee in deep regret, but he could do nothing now.

Moral: Presence of mind helps solve even the trickiest of problems.

97. THE THIRSTY ANT

A tear of a child once saved a thirsty ant. The ant realised it could now understand and speak the human language! Visiting a castle once, the ant found a little girl. It looked like she was crying for a long time. She told him that an ogre had imprisoned her. The ogre had told her to make three heaps of grain, rye, and barley out of huge mounds of seeds all mixed. She cried, "If I don't finish by tomorrow, he will have me for supper." The ant said he would help. He fetched all his friends, and they set to work. The next morning, the ogre found the three mounds he wanted! So, it was a tear that came to the rescue of a little girl!

Moral: Always help each other.

98. THE HEN THAT LAID SILVER EGGS

A woman caught a hen that laid silver eggs and thought, "If the hen could lay more than one egg each day, I would never have to work!" Therefore, she decided that the hen must eat more so that it could lay more eggs. So the woman forced the hen to eat a lot of food. The next morning, she hoped that the hen would have laid more than one egg. But she was shocked to find that her hen was dead. It had died of overeating, and the woman no longer got any silver eggs.

Moral: Don't be greedy. Always be happy with what and how much you have.

99. THE HUNTING DOG AND THE GUARD DOG

Once a man had two dogs. Even though the hunting dog got food from his master, it was the guard dog who got the tastiest morsels! The hunting dog complained to the guard dog one day, "This is not fair. I hunt all day long, while you get your food without doing any work." The guard dog replied, "That's up to the master. He feels it's more important to reward the protector of his home than the one that goes hunting with him."

Moral: Never complain about things that are wise and fair.

100. THE SPARROWS AND THE ELEPHANT

An elephant once broke all the eggs of a sparrow couple. The sparrow couple became sad and thought, "We must seek help from our friends." The crow couple, the frog, and the flies thought of a plan to teach the elephant a lesson. The next day, the flies flew near its' ears, making a buzzing sound. The crow couple jumped down and bit the elephant in both the eyes, making him blind. Just then, the frog croaked. Thinking he was close to a pond, the elephant went in that direction, but he ended up falling into a deep ditch.

Moral: Always be careful about what you are doing.

101. FELIX THE TERRIBLE AND THE FOX

Once, a fox met a cat in the forest and learnt it was Felix the Terrible. The fox spread the news that "Felix the Terrible, new governor is very wild!" To become friends with him, the bear took an ox for him, while the wolf took a sheep. As they were scared, they sent a hare to tell the governor first. The bear hid in a tree and the wolf in a hole. The cat attacked the hare. Just then, the wolf shifted, making a sharp sound. The cat got scared and jumped into the air, landing on the wolf's nose! The wolf quickly stood up and ran away! Since then, all the animals have been scared of cats.

Moral: Don't trust anyone, blindly.